Sam's Cat Jan

by Liza Charlesworth

ISBN: 978-1-338-84364-4

Art Director: Tannaz Fassihi; Designer: Cynthia Ng; Illustrated by Kevin Zimmer
Copyright © Liza Charlesworth. All rights reserved. Published by Scholastic Inc.

3 4 5 6 7 68 26 25 24

Printed in Jiaxing, China. First printing, June 2022.

■ SCHOLASTIC

Sam has a cat.
The cat is Jan.

Jan sat on a mat.
"Jan is sad," said Sam.

Sam got Jan a hat.
The cat got mad!

Sam got Jan a fan.
The cat got mad!

5

Sam got Jan a bag.
The bag had jam in it.

Jam got on Jan.
The cat got mad.
Mad, mad, mad!

7

Sam got Jan a pal.

8

Jan sat.
The pal sat.

Then Jan ran.
The pal ran.

Ran, ran, ran!

Ran, ran, ran!

Ran, ran, ran!

Then Jan and the pal
had a cat nap.

"Yes!" said Sam.
"Jan is not sad."

Read & Review

Invite your learner to point to each short-*a* word and read it aloud.

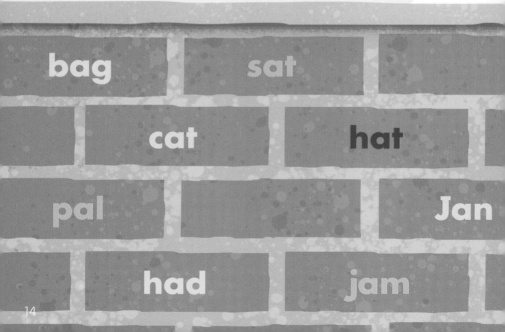

bag

sat

cat

hat

pal

Jan

had

jam

14

nap

ran

has

mat

Sam

mad

sad

fan

Fun Fill-Ins

Read the sentences aloud, inviting your learner to complete them using the short-*a* words in the box.

> pal   Sam   nap   jam   Jan

1. The name of the cat is _____.

2. The name of the boy is _____.

3. Jan did not like the _____.

4. Jan DID like to run with the _____.

5. At the end, Jan and the pal

   take a _____.